CONTENTS

COOL CRETACIA! 6

ALL ABOUT... GIGANTOSAURUS! 8

JOIN THE DINO DOTS 10

DINO DETECTIVES 11

ALL ABOUT... THE DEN! 12

CRETACIAN CROSSWORD 14

DINO DIFFERENCES 15

ALL ABOUT... ROCKY! 16

ROCKY, THE RECORD BREAKER 18

ROCKY'S RACE 22

MONSTER MATCHING 24

DINO JOKES 25

ALL ABOUT... TINY! 26

MIRROR, MIRROR 28

DINO DRAWINGS 32

ALL ABOUT... MAZU! 34

DINOS TO THE MOON 36

COLOURFUL CRETACIA 40

MAZU'S MAZE 42

ALL ABOUT... BILL! 44

CAPA-BILL 46

WHICH DINO ARE YOU? 50

ALL ABOUT... DINO FRIENDS! 52

WISH UPON A STAR 56

ROCKY MASK 57

TAR TROUBLE 59

SIBLING SILLINESS 60

ALL ABOUT...THE BADDIES! 62

DINO DICE 64

WACKY WORDS 66

LAZING BY THE LAKE 68

RACE TO GIGANTO! 70

MEMORY TEST 71

JIGSAW JAPES 73

CRETACIA QUIZ 74

PUZZLE ANSWERS.................. 76

THIS ANNUAL BELONGS TO...

_____

Published 2022.
Little Brother Books Ltd, Ground Floor,
23 Southernhay East, Exeter, Devon EX1 1QL
books@littlebrotherbooks.co.uk
www.littlebrotherbooks.co.uk

Printed in China. Xuantan Temple Industrial Zone,
Gulao Town, Heshan, Guangdong.

COOL

CRETACIA

Far away and long ago four dino friends are having lots of fun and adventures in Cretacia. Whether they're running, flying jet packs or being flipped into the air by Giganto's tail, Rocky, Tiny, Bill and Mazu love exploring this roar-inspiring land!

Cretacia is full of surprises: tar pits, lava, carnivorous plants - not to mention some new little siblings! But that doesn't stop the four friends from overcoming almost any obstacle with a little teamwork, courage and friendship.

BOOM BOOM BOOM

From jungle mazes and sticky swamps to cool lakes and a snowy glacier - Cretacia has no end of places to explore and the four dinos just keep making new discoveries.

STOMP

STOMP

STOMP

Though Giganto is the dino's friend, he is also the most mysterious and terrifying of all the dinos in Cretacia.

ALL ABOUT.... GIGANTOSAURUS!

GIGANTO

Giganto is one huge and fierce dino. He's a hero to Rocky, Tiny, Bill and Mazu but still a little scary. One thing's for sure – he packs the most enormous roar!

ROARRR!

Giganto has a knack for turning up just in time to help the four friends out of sticky situations.

Though big and scary, Giganto has a fun side. The four friends love nothing more than when he throws them into the air with his tail.

WEEEEEEEEEEE!

There's only one dinosaur who's as terrifying as Giganto and that's Spinosaurus: a lean, mean eating machine, with a sail on his back. The four friends know not to stand too close when he and Giganto come head to head!

Giganto's lair is an epic home for an epic dino. Would you like to live there?

JOIN THE DINO DOTS

Create a picture of Giganto by joining the dots. Colour him in with your most ferocious colours!

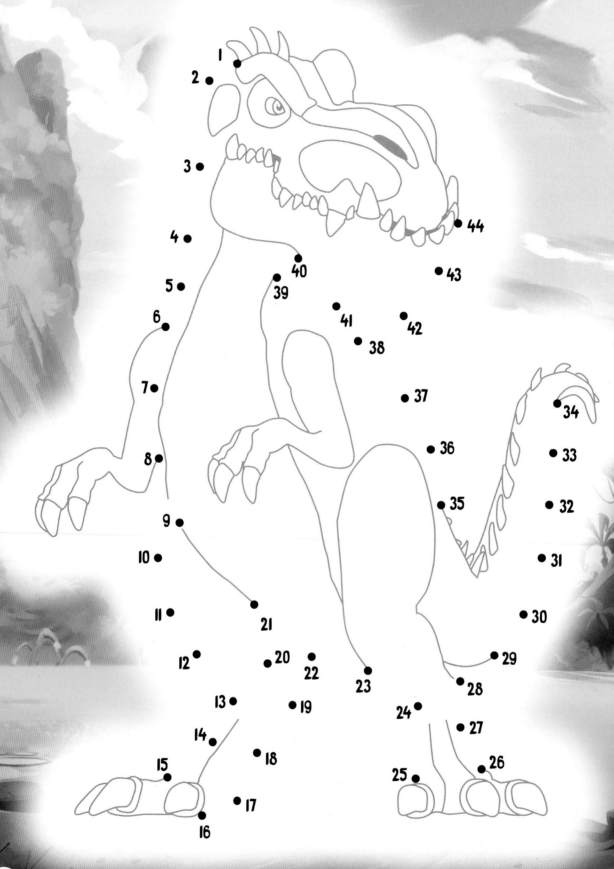

DINO DETECTIVES

What do Rocky, Tiny, Mazu and
Bill think of Giganto?
Break the dino code to find out.

ALL ABOUT... THE DEN!

With a garage, dormitory and view of a volcano, The dino's Den makes a pretty awesome home. Read on to find out more.

Roof garden: The dino friends like to hang out on The Den's roof, especially at night when it makes a stellar place to watch the stars.

THE DEN DORMITORY

The Mazmobile: When Mazu wants to go somewhere in a hurry, she jumps in the Mazmobile. It's super speedy and can fly!

THE DEN GARAGE

Can you spot these objects in this picture?
Tick them off as you find each one.

Cosy beds: After a day of adventures the four friends sleep on soft leaves in their cosy dormitory.

ZZZZZZZZzzz

How many flowers 🐝 can you count on these pages?

Is that an odd or an even number? Odd ☐ Even ☐

Colour in this dragonfly with your brightest pens!

CRETACIAN CROSSWORD

Read the clues to find the words in the crossword.

Hint:
The words are names of dinos or places!

Across
2. He's nervous, blue and always hungry.
3. He's adventurous and fast.
5. She's inventive, brown and stubborn.
6. A small and artistic dino.

Down
1. Big, scary and green!
4. The world the dinos' live in.

Write the letters from the crossword in the matching coloured boxes to find out what they spell.

DINO DIFFERENCES

Can you spot six differences in these two pictures?
Colour in a dino footprint as you find each one.

ANSWERS ON PAGES 76-77 15

ALL ABOUT... ROCKY!

ROCKY

Type: Parasaurolophus
Age: 9 and a half years old
Strengths: Running and being brave
Weaknesses: Patience and... being brave.
He's too brave sometimes!
Where you'll find him: Having adventures
with his friends, exploring the most
dangerous corners of Cretacia

If there's an adventure to be had Rocky is
always first off the mark. His bravery can land
him in sticky situations but with Bill, Mazu and
Tiny on the case they always find a solution -
sometimes with a little help from Giganto!

Giganto is Rocky's hero. Rocky would love to be as big, scary - and loud - as his gigantic pal. Though Giganto may not always seem to notice Rocky, he's always there when this plucky dino needs him most.

roaaawr!

Rocky has a very gentle side. He and his pals once found an egg and kept safe until it hatched into a baby Parasaurolophus - a cousin for Rocky! Rocky looks out for little Rolo whenever he can.

Although Rocky thinks he can handle any situation on his own, he's learned that things work out best when he's with his friends.

ROCKY, THE RECORD BREAKER

The friends discover a monument to Roger the Record Breaker, a legendary dino who broke 99 records! Rocky has an idea...

I'm gonna break all Roger's records!

So Rocky attempts: most pineapples snuck past carnivorous plants, longest push of a slippery stegosaurus, biggest tree ever lifted, longest time plugging up a geyser and most coconuts ever juggled...

MMMGHH!

... but he doesn't break a single record.

Mazu is doubtful.

These records are impossible!

Rocky is cross. He thinks he could break the records if his friends weren't there.

You're bad luck!

Rocky attempts to break one more record... wrestling Giganto's tail.

But Giganto flips Rocky into the air...

... and he lands in a crevice.

We'll help you Rocky!

The friends make a dino chain to try to lift Rocky out but they fall in too.

BUMMPF!

Luckily Giganto lifts the dinos out with his tail and flicks them into the air.

WOOOSH!

Rocky says sorry. He realises that some things are more important than breaking records and that he's already broken the record for...

AWWWW

Having the best friends ever!

ROCKY'S RACE

Race your friends around Cretacia, following the instructions when you land on the squares.

START HERE

19 Follow the footprints to space 22.

20

21

18

17

16 Stop to ride on a geyser. Miss a go.

15

14

1

2

3 You find your jetpack which gives you a headstart. Move forward three spaces.

4

5

6

7 Eek! Run away from some hungry carnivorous plants! Miss a go!

8

WHAT TO DO:
1. Cut out the counters below.
2. Throw the dice and move your counters around the board following the instructions as you land on each one.

22

23
Boom!
The volcano has erupted and you have to dodge some lava. Go back three spaces.

FINISH!

31

30

29
You eat some delicious berries which give you lots of energy. Speed to the Finish.

24

13

25
Get flipped into the air by Giganto's tail. Fly forward three spaces.

12

28

11

26

27

10
Speed down the river on a boat. Move forward two spaces.

9

Always ask an adult for help with using scissors. If you don't want to cut up your book, ask an adult to photocopy or scan this page.

MONSTER MATCHING

Match these dino friends to their shadows. Draw a line between each matching pair.

Colour in the blank footprints in red, green or blue to complete the sequences.

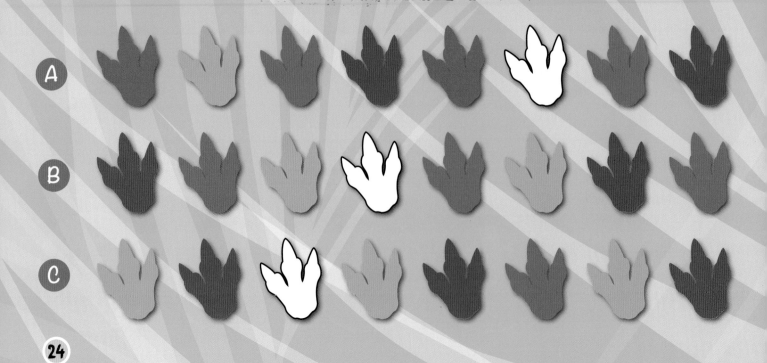

DINO JOKES

Tiny is telling some funny jokes. Can you help her by drawing lines between each joke and its punchline?

1 What do you call a dino who's a noisy sleeper?

A Because it won't shut!

2 Which dinosaur has to wear glasses?

3 What did the dinosaur use to build his house?

B A scare-a-dactyl!

4 How do you invite a dinosaur to a cafe?

C Tyrannosaurus specs.

D A dino-snore!

E Tea, Rex?

5 What do you call a dinosaur ghost?

6 How do you know there's a dinosaur in your fridge?

F A dino-saw!

ALL ABOUT... TINY!

Type: Triceratops
Age: 9 years old
Strengths: Being artistic and telling jokes!
Weaknesses: She doesn't take life seriously - which can be dangerous in Cretacia!
Where you'll find her: Out decorating something with her drawings

Tiny's positivity, silliness and creative thinking make her a fun friend. Combine that with her Triceratops strength and she's a useful dino to have on an adventure.

Tiny is very artistic and will paint onto just about anything, mixing up berries and other fruit to make bright colours. She loves nature and finds lots of things beautiful, but her favourite thing to paint is her friends!

According to Tiny's big brother Trey, Triceratops should be big, strong warriors. But, as Tiny says, she's more of a dancer than a warrior! Tiny and Trey's differences don't hold them back from getting along. And now they have their little sister Tory to look out for, they're closer than ever before.

Tiny is a good and loyal friend. Before the dinos knew that Giganto could be trusted, Tiny was keen to give him a chance. She sees the good in everyone - except, maybe Spinosaurus!

MIRROR, MIRROR

Tiny is on a mission to paint the perfect family portrait but gets distracted by her own reflection!

Tiny was painting a family portrait. 'Did I get myself right?' she asked her friends, revealing the picture. 'Hmm, interesting,' said Mazu politely. Rocky was less tactful, 'Is that supposed to be you or a giant pickle?' Tiny was upset. She didn't have a mirror and couldn't see what she looked like. 'How can I paint myself if I can't see myself?' she said sadly.

'Don't worry Tiny, there's always a solution,' Mazu said walking away, 'I'll be right back.' Mazu returned later with a shiny stone. 'It's a look-see,' she said. The dinos passed it around, admiring their reflections. 'Wow!' sighed Tiny. 'I've never seen myself so clearly. That's magic!' 'No,' explained Mazu. 'That's science!'

The four dinos set off to look for berries to make paint. Tiny liked looking at her reflection so much that she kept bumping into things... and dinos. 'Oops sorry!' she said to Iggy, as she stumbled into him. When they got to the berry bush, the dinos started picking berries. But Tiny was too busy looking at her reflection to help them. 'It might be easier if I hold that,' said Bill. Tiny reluctantly agreed and handed over the mirror.

When the four friends had picked enough berries they started to walk home. Their route took them past some big holes in the ground. 'I just want one.. more.. look..' said Tiny, jumping up to see over Bill's shoulder, but she bumped into him and they fell into a hole! 'Arrrrgh!' they shouted as they bumped and slid their way towards the bottom. 'We're coming to save you!' said Rocky, grabbing Mazu and jumping in after them. 'Prepare to be saved!'

The dinos tumbled out into the sunlight... and right into the path of some dino-eating plants! They didn't know how to get past them. 'We're going to bust right through those big bullies!' said Rocky bravely, marching up to the plants but getting caught straight away. 'This is all my fault', said Tiny. 'I should've been paying attention instead of looking at myself. I'm so sorry.'

Suddenly the ground shook and there was a scritch-scratching noise. It was Giganto, rubbing his back against a tree. 'Help!' cried Tiny, Bill and Mazu, jumping up and down to try to get the big dino's attention, but he couldn't hear them! 'I've got an idea!' said Tiny.

Tiny grabbed the mirror. 'I've just... got to... catch a sunbeam.' The mirror caught the sunlight and Tiny angled it towards Giganto's eyes. 'Rwoaurrr!' growled Giganto, and followed the light to the trapped dinos. Immediately, he sprang into action, jumping into the air and landing with a ground-shaking thud. Below his feet the ground cracked and a crater formed, swallowing the scary plants whole. 'Wooooah!' said Rocky, as he flew through the air to safety.

Back at The Den, Tiny revealed her amazing new painting. This time, her friends loved it. 'Thanks for including us in your family portrait!' said Bill. Tiny thought they deserved to be in the picture. 'You guys really looked out for me today - just like family would.' Just then, Giganto came along and Tiny had another idea. 'I think I can squeeze you in too Giganto - smile!'

DINO DRAWINGS

These colours are dino-mite!

Help Tiny finish these paintings of her friends. Draw over the lines and then give your pictures some colour.

TINY

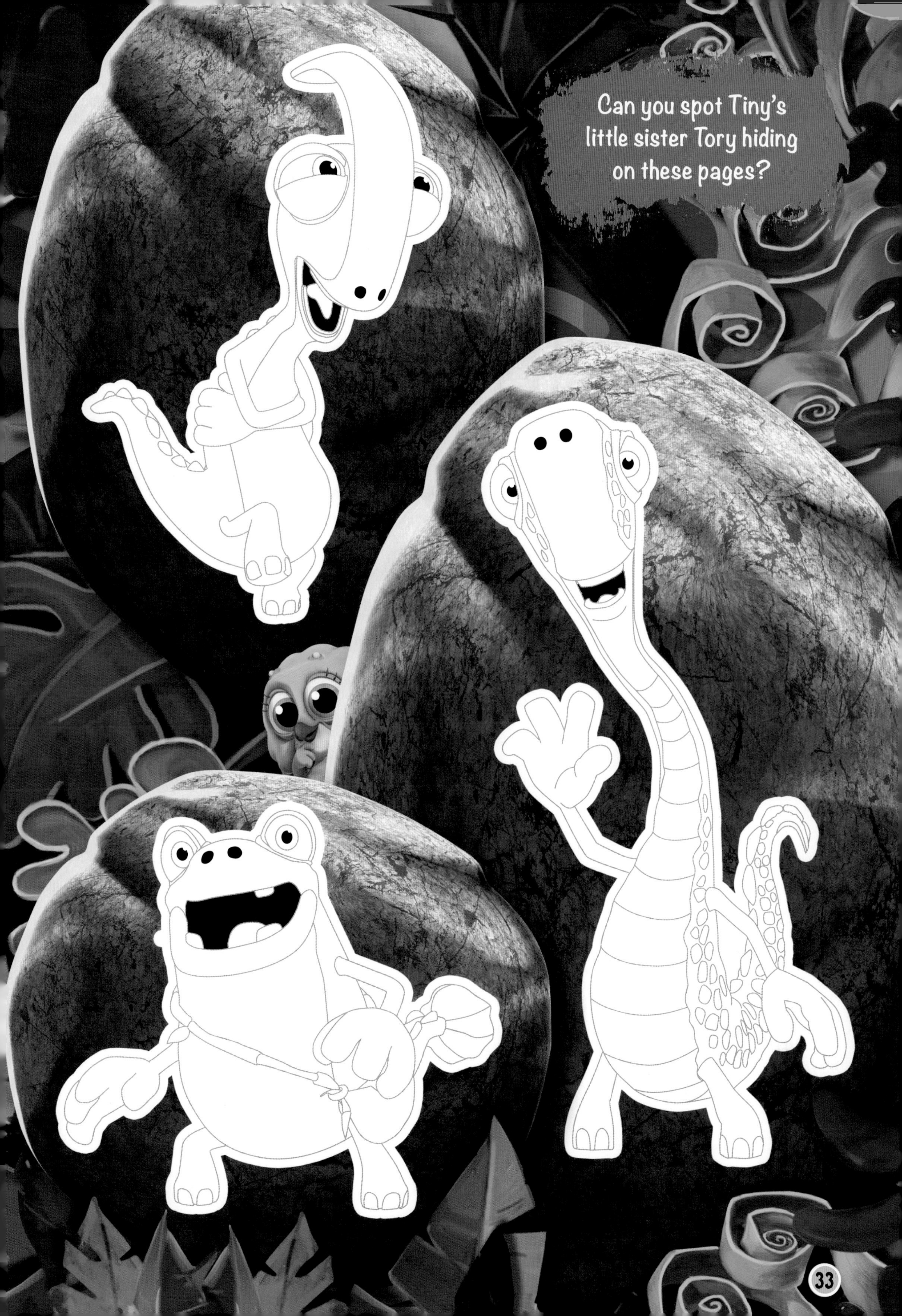
Can you spot Tiny's little sister Tory hiding on these pages?

ALL ABOUT... MAZU!

Mazu has a cool tail club which is so hard it can be used as a hammer!

Type: Ankylosaurus
Age: 9 and a half years old
Strengths: Her inventiveness
Weaknesses: Being stubborn
Where you'll find her: Out looking for her next big discovery

Mazu is one smart Ankylosaurus. She loves inventing things and studying the world around her. Her most exciting inventions yet are the crystal powered jet packs that she and her friends have used on adventures!

Mazu's curiosity has led her to make lots of brilliant discoveries, but sometimes she gets herself into dangerous situations in the name of science!

Mazu is very protective of smaller creatures, including her baby brother Zak. Once, by using her brains, and some well placed raptor traps, she rescued a rare dragonfly from meanies Totor and Cror.

While Mazu brings the brains - and some really cool inventions - to their adventures, she knows she can always count on Rocky, Tiny and Bill for their encouragement and friendship.

DINOS TO THE MOON

MAZU

Mazu attempts to do what no dino has ever done before - fly to the moon!

One morning Mazu revealed her most impressive invention yet - a space rocket! She explained that she'd always wanted to fly to the moon and hoped the rocket would take them all there. 'Wow!' said her friends in unison. 'When can we go?' Mazu told them to prepare for training. 'Get ready for the challenge of a lifetime,' she told them. 'You're going to become dinastronauts!'

Mazu tested the pressure of take off by catapulting Rocky into the air. 'Pressure's my middle naaa-aame!' he shouted as he flew away from them. Tiny was pushed down a hill in a big bubble to prepare her for a bumpy space flight. 'Nailed it!' said Tiny, as she came to a standstill, her eyes rolling around in her head. Bill tested weightlessness by being spun around very fast. 'I love being a dinastronaut!' he said afterwards, falling to the ground in a dizzy heap.

Finally, the dinos completed their training. 'I can't believe we're going to be the first dinos on the moon!' said Rocky. 'I can't believe I agreed to this,' chipped in Bill. Mazu had built a special chute to launch the rocket. 'Lift off!' cried Mazu, and the dinos wooshed into the sky! The rocket was fast at first but lost power and started falling back to earth. A parachute opened and they made a soft landing in an unexplored corner of Cretacia.

The rocket had landed in a sort of jungly maze, with flowers growing out of high walls and vines hanging down. When they explored, they found Giganto taking a shower under a waterfall and a beautiful cave of crystals, but Mazu was a little sad. 'I didn't get us to the moon and now we're lost,' she said. 'I'm a failure!' Tiny didn't agree. 'If you don't fail sometimes, how will you learn?'

The friends stared in awe at the crystals. Mazu took a crystal and found that it had a reaction with water. When it touched water, the crystal bubbled and fizzed and shot into the air - just like a rocket! 'We can use the crystals to power the rocket!' said Mazu, starting to collect as many as she could. Now all they needed was water.

Mazu took a clay pot to the waterfall but she slipped and broke the pot. 'Don't give up Mazu,' she told herself. 'This isn't a failure, it's just a setback!' Giganto saw what happened and used his tail to direct the water from the waterfall towards the crystals at the bottom of the rocket. 'Thanks Giganto!' Mazu cried, as she ran towards the rocket and jumped on board.

This time the rocket took off with extra force, leaving a pink bubbly trail of gas in the night sky behind them. Mazu looked hopefully at the moon through the rocket window as it grew bigger and brighter. But then, slowly, as before, the rocket lost power, slowed down, and started to fall back to earth. 'Oh,' Mazu sighed.

'Are you ok?' Tiny asked Mazu kindly when they landed. 'I'm fine,' smiled Mazu. 'Maybe we didn't get to the moon, but the trip was filled with so many discoveries. And we got so much closer the second time. I'll just keep trying!' 'That's the spirit,' yawned Bill, as the dinos headed to bed. Mazu was tired but happy. 'One day all I've learned will help me, or someone, get to the moon!'

COLOURFUL CRETACIA

Colour in the four best buds with your brightest pens!

MAZU'S MAZE

Help Mazu find her friends at the end of The Maze. Collect crystals and avoid obstacles like scary Spinosaurus, who is lurking down one of the paths!

START

How many crystals did you collect? Write the number in the box.

ALL ABOUT... BILL!

Type: Brachiosaurus
Age: 7 years old
Strengths: Good sense of smell and a very long neck, which is perfect for being on the lookout!
Weaknesses: Hiding behind the nearest rock when he's scared
Where you'll find him: Looking for his next snack!

Bill is a very timid dinosaur, but he doesn't let that stop him from joining his friends on adventures. Plus, he has the Bill Bubble - a very cool vehicle that can go underwater!

Bill can be brave when he needs to. Before the dinos knew Giganto was friendly (and Bill was absolutely terrified of him) the little dino once faced his fears to rescue Tiny who was trapped behind Giganto's tail.

Juicy blueberries, sweet pineapples, chewy coconuts: you name it - Bill can sniff out most food growing in Cretacia. Bill loves food so much that he's even been known to eat in his sleep!

Bill is a friend you can count on. He is also great at giving hugs!

Bill has a cute little sister called Leena!

BILL

CAPA-BILL

Mazu shows the dinos and Leon her new invention – a crystal powered jetpack!

Wowww!!

Mazu has made jetpacks for everyone, but they need to collect crystals to power them.

Let's go to the maze!

The friends cross a river on a slippery log.

Bill crosses nervously... and slips... onto Leon's back!

Thank's Leon!

I like helping dinos.

When they reach the crystals, Bill struggles to lift them...

NNNNNNGH!!

... so Leon pushes Bill and the crystals.

I could've done that without Leon's help.

Tiny and Rocky try out their new jetpacks.

SWOOSH!!

Nervously, Bill closes his eyes and... feels like he's flying... but Leon has carried them both onto Giganto's tail! Bill is upset.

I'll never learn to do things for myself if you keep helping me!

Sorry Bill.

Later, Bill and Leon hear a rumbling sound. The volcano is erupting! Lava is flowing towards them faster than Leon can walk.

Bill thinks quickly. He sees a hollow log and uses it to push Leon along...

You can do it Bill!

... then carries Leon over a crevice using his jetpack.

Later, Leon tells the dinos how Bill saved him and they're amazed.

From now on I'm gonna call you Capa-Bill

WHICH DINO ARE YOU?

Take this quiz to find out!

Do you like science?

NO

YES

Are you good at art?

YES

NO

Can you be stubborn sometimes?

YES

Are you good at inventing things?

NO

Are you quite confident and positive?

YES

YES

MAZU

Like Mazu, you're super smart and you love trying to make sense of the world. With your friends close by you're an unstoppable force of nature!

TINY

You're creative and kind. You love to look at beautiful things, and, like Tiny's paintings, you often reflect the brighter side of life.

START
Are you often the first person to raise your hand when your teacher asks a question at school?

NO

Do you get a little nervous sometimes?

NO

YES

Do you love food almost more than you love your friends?

NO

YES

Are you good at running?

NO

YES

Do you have a good sense of smell?

YES

Would you choose food over fun?

NO

NO

Do you often jump into situations head first?

NO

YES

YES

YES

BILL

You're a sensitive dino like Bill, which can make you a little nervous sometimes. You're very kind and you can be brave when a friend's in trouble.

ROCKY

You're super brave and always looking for an adventure. This can sometimes get you into tricky situations, but if you're as lucky as Rocky, you know your friends will always have your back!

ALL ABOUT... DINO FRIENDS!

Cretacia is home to a host of fun and friendly creatures. Meet some of them here.

TREY

Tiny's brother Trey calls himself the 'roughest, toughest Triceratops in all of Cretacia'. While he is very strong, he can also be playful and silly with his little sister Tiny.

LEON

A turtle-like amphibious creature, Leon walks (very slowly) on land but speeds through water in the lake where he lives. Leon is the same age as the four dinos and is a bright, optimistic and resourceful friend.

ARCHIE

Nervous and alert, Archie makes a good lookout. Sadly for him, he has wings, but is unable to fly. That doesn't stop him trying... and failing... with painful consequences.

THE ICHTHYOSAURS

A group of colourful Cretacian dolphins, Plink, Plonk and Plunk are playful and friendly. They share the lake with Leon and Termy.

Plink

Plonk   Plunk

HEGAN

Hegan is a pterosaur who can fly super-fast and has been known to carry the dino friends on her back!

MARSHALL

Though bigger than the four dinos, Marshall is younger than them. He has a strong spiky tail, which is useful when playing ball games.

AYATI

A brachiosaurus like Bill, Ayati is the oldest and wisest of the dinos' friends and loves to tell them stories from her life. She is so tall that her neck makes an excellent slide!

TERMY

This lake bound monster isn't exactly a friend of the dinos. There was a time when The Terminatotor, or Termy for short, would have happily gobbled them up as a snack. She's more friendly since the four friends helped her return from the frozen land, but she can still keep them on their toes.

RUGO

Rugo, the Rugosodon, likes eating almost as much as Bill does and is a good friend to the dinos. Her skills include storing food in her cheeks, fitting through small spaces and burrowing.

WISH UPON A STAR

The dinos are making wishes every time they see a shooting star.
Can you guess what they wish for?
Draw lines between the characters and their wishes.

1 I wish I could make a really important discovery for science!

2 I wish I could see one of those stars up close!

3 I want to paint the stars!

4 My wish is to find a super huge coconut to make more coco chips!

What would you wish for? Write your answer below.

ROCKY MASK

Make like Rocky and create this roar-some mask!

1. Carefully cut along the dotted lines. Cut out the eye and side holes. Always ask an adult for help with using scissors.
2. Measure and cut a length of string to fit around the back of your head.
3. Feed the ends of the string through the side holes and secure them with knots.
4. Tie the mask around your head and channel your inner Rocky!

Don't want to cut up your book? Ask an adult to photocopy or scan this page.

Colour the back of your mask
with your brightest red pens!

TAR TROUBLE

Splat! These characters have been covered with sticky tar. Can you guess who they are? Choose your answers from the names below and write them under the pictures.

Tiny   Archie   Rugo
Rocky   Trey

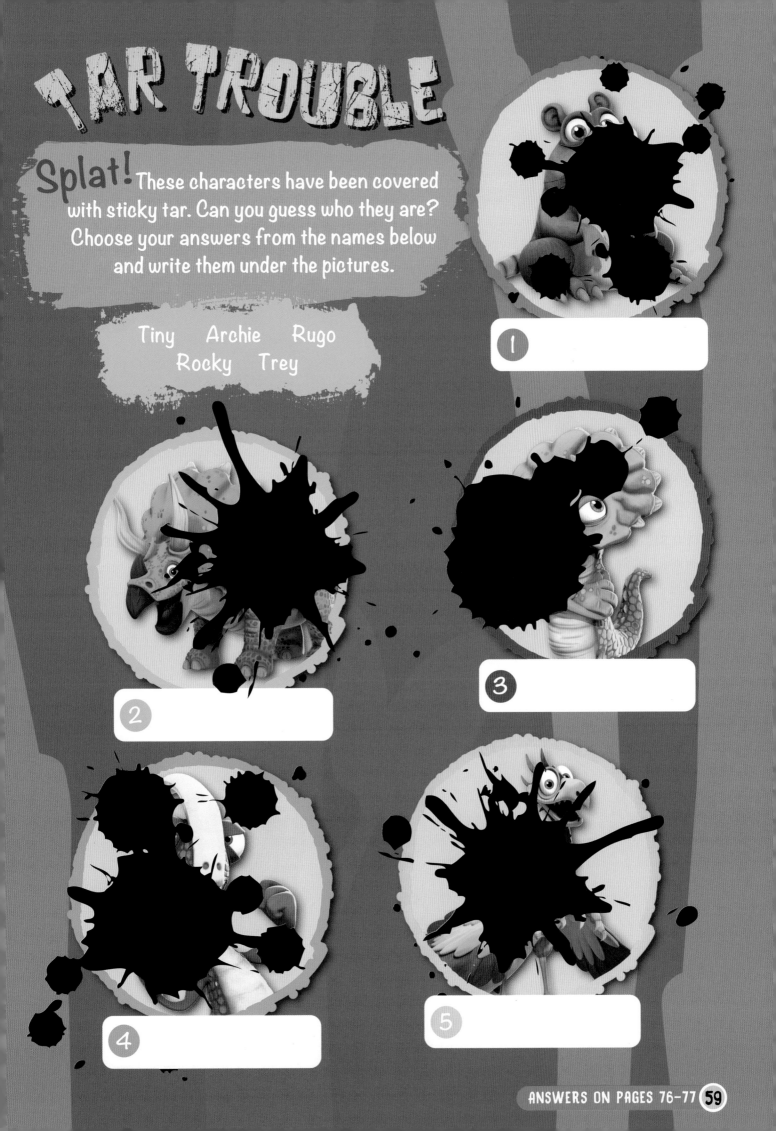

1

2

3

4

5

SIBLING SILLINESS

Bill, Mazu and Tiny know it can be really fun (and sometimes tricky) to have a little sibling. Trace the letters to write the baby dinos' names.

Leena

Bill's
little sister

Zak

Mazu's
little brother

Tory

Tiny's
little sister

Rolo

Rocky's
little cousin

CRETACIA COUNTING

How many baby dinos can you count in this pile? Write the number in the box.

Being a big sister has its challenges, but I love my little 'Tory Dinosaury'!

SILLY SONG

Tiny's brother Trey is singing a song to their baby sister Tory. Help him by choosing song words from the list and writing them in the correct spaces.

The tune for this song is the same as for 'Wheels on the Bus'.

Giganto's feet go up and down,

_ _ and down,

Up and _ _ _ _ ,

_ _ _ _ _ _ _ _ _ _ _ _ _ _ _ _ go _ _ _ _ _ _ _ _ _ ,

All through Cretacia!

Giganto's feet	Up	Up and down	Around
Tiny's ears	Jumping around	Sideways	Down

ALL ABOUT... THE BADDIES!

Although our four heroes have a lot of fun in Cretacia there are plenty of things – and creatures – to keep them on their toes!

ROOOOAAARRR!!!

Although he may seem indestructible, Spinosaurus has a few weaknesses: he's easily distracted; his size makes him slow and awkward; and if the wind catches the sail on his back he could topple over!

SPINOSAURUS

BOOM BOOM BOOM, here comes Spino! Perhaps the biggest, baddest, dino of them all, Spinosaurus is Giganto's only true nemesis. He roams around eating whatever he wants and challenging anyone who gets in his way.

TUTOR AND GROR

These two meanies are always out looking for trouble. Luckily, they can be easily outwitted - especially by Mazu!

THUD THUD THUD

T-REX

T the teenage T-Rex is a bit of a tough guy. He likes to think he's as big and strong as Giganto but he's quick to make up excuses for not going anywhere near him!

DINO DICE

Create and play this fun dice game with your friends!

WHAT TO DO:

1. Cut around the dotted edges. Always ask a grown up for help with using scissors and glue.
2. Fold the dice, including the flaps at the edges.
3. Stick the flaps together using the glue and wait for your dice to dry.
4. Throw the dice and follow the instructions of the side that lands face up.
5. Have fun!

YOU WILL NEED:
1 or more friends
Scissors
Glue

Roar and stomp your feet like Giganto!

If you don't want to cut up your book, ask an adult to photocopy or scan this page.

Tiny loves jokes. Tell your friends your best joke.

Think like Mazu and come up with an invention – the sillier the better!

Flap your wings like Archie and caw like a bird.

Rocky really can run! Run up and down the room three times.

Bill can be a little nervous. Imagine you've seen something scary and do your tiniest, quietest little roar!

WACKY WORDS

Bill loves making up new words. Make your own dino-fabulous creations by drawing lines between the two columns below.

Awesome	-tastic
Dino	-fabulous
Fan	-most
Awe	-ly
Fab	-ish
Cool	-y
Giganto	- est
Amazing	- some
Amaze	- dabbydozy
Best	- arama

Awesome-most is my new favourite word!

Write your Giganto-tastic combinations below or make up your own!

Can you find these Cretacian creatures, dinos and objects in the wordsearch? Tick the boxes and cross the word out as you find each one.

A	D	M	A	R	S	H	A	L	L
R	L	E	U	F	N	O	N	U	O
P	L	A	N	T	I	E	Y	R	H
L	H	M	R	H	D	A	Y	U	K
U	S	D	C	A	C	F	H	G	C
N	Z	A	A	R	K	L	M	O	M
K	E	T	R	E	Y	O	L	E	T
P	E	O	C	C	R	W	O	H	O
U	L	H	H	A	H	E	R	A	T
R	U	N	I	L	N	R	D	Q	O
B	L	U	E	B	E	R	R	Y	R

A

B

C

D

E

Trey

Marshall

Totor

Blueberry

Plunk

Plant

Archie

Rugo

Flower

Peach

Bill loves eating and has collected these yummy peaches. Can you number them from 1 for the smallest to 5 for the biggest?

LAZING BY THE LAKE

Can you spot these creatures and objects in the picture? Tick them off as you spot each one.

The dino friends are hanging out at the lake. Join them with these fun activities.

Rocky's feeling a little off colour. Add some reds to brighten him up!

How many lily pads can you see in the picture? Write the number in the box.

Is this an odd or even number?
◯ Odd ◯ Even

RACE TO GIGANTO!

Rocky, Bill, Tiny and Mazu are visiting Giganto. Follow the trails with your finger to find out who reaches him first.

BILL   **TINY**   **MAZU**   **ROCKY**

MEMORY TEST

Look at this picture for three minutes then test your memory by answering the questions on the next page.

MEMORY TEST

What can you remember about the picture?
Test your memory with these questions.

1 What colour are the flowers Tiny has picked?
a) Pink ☐
b) Blue ☐
c) Yellow ☐

2 What emotion do you think Bill is feeling?
a) Happy ☐
b) Scared ☐
c) Tired ☐

3 What is Bill holding in his hand?
a) A blueberry ☐
b) A butterfly ☐
c) A torch ☐

4 What is Rocky laying on?
a) A bed ☐
b) Some grass ☐
c) A big leaf ☐

5 What is Mazu holding?
a) A dragonfly ☐
b) A stone ☐
c) A magnifying glass ☐

6 What are the colours of the dragonfly Mazu is holding?
a) Rainbow colours ☐
b) Black ☐
c) Blue and yellow ☐

7 How many lily pads were there on the pond?
a) Two ☐
b) Four ☐
c) One ☐

8 How many blue pools of water did you count?
a) One ☐
b) Four ☐
c) Nine ☐

JIGSAW JAPES

What's Rocky doing? Find out by linking the jigsaw pieces to the correct spaces.

Colour a footprint as you match each puzzle piece to its space.

CRETACIA QUIZ

Test your knowledge of the world of Gigantosaurus with this fun quiz!

1

What is Rocky's best skill?

a) Singing ☐
b) Running ☐
c) Knitting ☐

2

What is Bill most likely to be doing?

a) Eating ☐
b) Talking to Spinosaurus ☐
c) Sleeping ☐

3

Where do the dinos live?

a) Paleo-land ☐
b) Gigantosauria ☐
c) Cretacia ☐

4

What is Mazu's greatest wish?

a) To make a big discovery ☐
b) To climb a mountain ☐
c) To play all day with her friends ☐

5

What is the name of this Cretacian creature?

a) Lugo ☐
b) Rugo ☐
c) Ratty ☐

6

What is this baddy called?

a) Rhinosaurous ☐

b) Gigantosaurus ☐

c) Spinosaurus ☐

7

What is Tiny's favourite activity?

a) Fighting ☐

b) Painting ☐

c) Swimming ☐

8

What is the name of Rocky's vehicle?

a) The Rock-mobile ☐

b) The Rocky-roadster ☐

c) The Rocky Racer ☐

9

What is the name of the dino's house?

a) The Den ☐

b) The Treehouse ☐

c) The Dino Den ☐

10

Who's this friend of the dinos?

a) Alfie ☐

b) Archie ☐

c) Marshall ☐

HOW MANY DID YOU GET RIGHT?

1-3:   Excellent effort!

3-5:   You're making good progress on your dino discovery

6-10: You're a Gigantosaurus master!

ANSWERS ON PAGES 76-77

ANSWERS

PAGE 10 - JOIN THE DINO DOTS

PAGE 11 - DINO DETECTIVES

The dinos think: 'Giganto is roar-some!'

PAGE 12-13 - ALL ABOUT... THE DEN!

There are 8 flowers.
This is an even number.

PAGE 14 - CRETACIAN CROSSWORD

1. Giganto   2. Bill
3. Rocky   4. Cretacia
5. Mazu   6. Tiny
The secret word is TEAM

PAGE 15 - DINO DIFFERENCES

PAGE 24 - MONSTER MATCHING

PAGE 25 - DINO JOKES

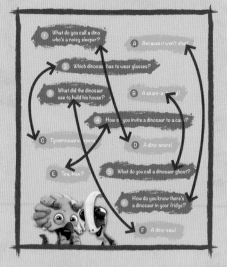

PAGE 32-33 - DINO DRAWINGS

PAGE 42-43 - MAZU'S MAZE

There are 8 crystals to collect in the maze.

PAGE 56 - WISH UPON A STAR

1. Mazu
2. Rocky
3. Tiny
4. Bill

PAGE 59 - TAR TROUBLE

1. Rugo
2. Trey
3. Tiny
4. Rocky
5. Archie

PAGE 60 - CRETACIA COUNTING

There are 9 baby dinos in the pile.

PAGE 61 - SILLY SONG

The correct words for the song puzzle are:

Giganto's feet go up and down,

Up and down,

Up and **down**,

Giganto's feet go **up and down**,

All through Cretacia!

PAGE 67 - WACKY WORDS

PAGE 67 - SIZE ORDERING PUZZLE

1. - D
2. - E
3. - B
4. - C
5. - A

PAGE 68 - LAZING BY THE LAKE

There are 10 Lily pads on the lake. This is an even number.

PAGE 70 - RACE TO GIGANTO!

PAGE 72 - MEMORY TEST

1. b) Tiny has picked pink flowers.
2. b) Bill is feeling scared.
3. c) He is holding a torch.
4. c) Rocky is laying on a leaf.
5. a) Mazu is holding a dragonfly.
6. c) It is blue and yellow.
7. a) There are two lily pads on the pond.
8. b) There are four raised blue pools of water.

PAGE 73 - JIGSAW JAPES

PAGE 74-75 - CRETACIA QUIZ

1. b) Running
2. a) Eating
3. c) Cretacia
4. a) To make a big discovery
5. b) Rugo
6. c) Spinosaurus
7. b) Painting
8. c) The Rocky Racer
9. a) The Den
10. b) Archie